Raffi Songs to Read®

DOWN BY THE BAY

Illustrated by Nadine Bernard Westcott

Crown Publishers • New York

For Bill—N.W.

Library of Congress Cataloging-in-Publication Data

Raffi. Down by the bay.
Summary: Down by the bay two young friends make up fantastic rhymes trying to top the other.
1. Children's songs. [1. Songs] I. Title
M1998.R 87-750 91

ISBN 0-517-56644-3 (trade) 10 9 8 7 6
    0-517-56645-1 (pbk.) 36 35 34 33 32 31 30 29 28

Originally published in hardcover in 1987
First paperback edition, February 1990

Front cover author photo © David Street
Back cover author photo © Patrick Harbron

 This book is printed on chlorine-free paper

DOWN BY THE BAY

Down by the bay, where the watermelons grow,
Back to my home I dare not go.

For if I do my mother will say,

"Did you ever see a goose kissing a moose,
Down by the bay?"

Down by the bay,
where the watermelons grow,
Back to my home I dare not go

For if I do my mother will say,

"Did you ever see a whale with a polka-dot tail,
Down by the bay?"

Down by the bay, where the watermelons grow,
Back to my home I dare not go.

For if I do my mother will say,

"Did you ever see a fly wearing a tie,
Down by the bay?"

Down by the bay, where the watermelons grow,
Back to my home I dare not go.

For if I do my mother will say,

"Did you ever see a bear combing his hair,
   Down by the bay?"

Down by the bay, where the watermelons grow,
Back to my home I dare not go.

For if I do my mother will say,

"Did you ever see llamas eating their pajamas,
Down by the bay?"

Down by the bay,
where the watermelons grow,
Back to my home I dare not go.
For if I do my mother will say,

"Did you ever see an **apple**...
wearing a **bapple**?"

"Did you ever see an **orange**...
eating a **blouse**?"

"Did you ever have a time when
you couldn't make a rhyme,
Down by the bay?"

DOWN BY THE BAY

Traditional

Down by the bay, where the wa-ter-mel-ons grow,
Back to my home I dare not go,
For if I do my mother will say, "Did you
ev - er see a goose kiss-ing a moose, Down by the bay."

2. Did you ever see a whale with a polka-dot tail...
3. Did you ever see a fly wearing a tie...
4. Did you ever see a bear combing his hair,
5. Did you ever see llamas eating their pajamas...
6. Did you ever have a time when you couldn't make a rhyme...
Down by the bay.